Disney's Year Book 1981

Disney's Year Book

1981

GROLIER ENTERPRISES, INC.
Danbury, Connecticut

GROLIER ENTERPRISES, INC.
Robert B. Clarke   *Publisher*

ISBN: 0-7172-8160-4
ISSN: 0273-1274

Illustration Credits and Acknowledgments

6—Thomas Zimmermann/FPG; 7—Steven E. Sutton/Duomo; 9—Focus on
Sports; 22—Boston Children's Museum; 23–28—Steve Rosenthal; 46—Joan
Lebold Cohen/Photo Researchers; 47—Allan Power/Bruce Coleman; 48—
© Joseph Van Wormer/Bruce Coleman; 49—Jeff Foott/Photo Researchers;
52—Peter D. Capen/Terra Mar Productions; 53—Peter D. Capen/Terra Mar
Productions; © Chesher/Photo Researchers; 54—Barry E. Parker/
Bruce Coleman: © 1978 John C. Deitz/Photo Researchers; 56—Jane Burton/
Bruce Coleman; Soames Summerhays/Photo Researchers; 57—Peter D.
Capen/Terra Mar Productions; 58—Peter D. Capen/Terra Mar Productions;
59–61—Michèle McLean; 62–63—© 1978 William Hubbell; 65–67—Michèle
McLean; 80—© Soames Summerhays/Photo Researchers; 81—© Kjell B.
Sanved/Photo Researchers; 83—© Robert C. Hermes/Photo Researchers

Contents

Golden Winter Games   6

Trailer Trouble   10

"Come Play with Me!"   22

A Two-Mile Hot Dog   30

Bibbidi-Bobbidi-Who?   34

Animals in Danger   46

Coral Rainbows under the Sea   51

Give a Box Some Beans   59

The Spookiest Park   62

Paint a Glass   65

Pinocchio Goes to Sea   68

Making Friends with a Shark   80

The Enchanted Figs   84

Golden Winter Games

The best athlete from any country at the 1980 Winter Olympics was American speedskater Eric Heiden. There are five speedskating races in the Olympics—the 500 meter, the 1,000 meter, the 1,500 meter, the

5,000 meter, and the 10,000 meter. Eric Heiden won them all!

It was the first time in the history of the Winter Olympics that an athlete had ever won five gold medals by himself. The great American swimmer, Mark Spitz, won seven medals in the 1972 Summer Olympics. But he only won four of the seven by himself. The other three were awarded to Spitz as one member of a team.

The XIII Winter Olympics were held at Lake Placid, New York, in February 1980.

Left: Eric Heiden raced to victory in speedskating.
Below: Phil Mahre won a silver medal in the slalom.

Athletes from 37 countries came to the Olympics. They competed in the usual Winter Olympic events, including skating, skiing, sledding, and playing hockey.

The United States scored a great victory in the hockey competition. No one thought that the United States team had a chance to win a gold medal in hockey. The Russian team was the favorite. In a game before the Olympics began, the Russians beat the American team by a score of 10-3.

But in the Olympics, it was a different story. The Americans won six of the seven games they played. They tied the other one. The most exciting game was between America and Russia. Millions of people watched on television as the two teams played hard.

Russia took the lead twice, 2-1 and 3-2. But each time the American team tied the score. In the last period, America scored a goal to win 4-3. Then, on the final day of the contest, the United States beat Finland, 4-2. That victory gave the United States the gold medal in hockey.

Russia and America battled for a gold medal in hockey.

America won 12 medals—six gold, four
silver, and two bronze. One of the silver
medals went to figure skater Linda Fratianne.
Another went to skier Phil Mahre.

Other countries won more medals than the
United States. East Germany had 23. Russia
had 22. But Americans will remember the XIII
Winter Olympics at Lake Placid for the gold
medals of speedskater Eric Heiden and the
United States hockey team.

TRAILER TROUBLE

Donald Duck hopped out of his car. "All ready to go?" he asked his nephews, Huey, Dewey, and Louie.

Donald's car was pulling a trailer loaded with modern gadgets. Huey, Dewey, and Louie looked at it in surprise. "Gosh, Uncle Donald! What's *that?*" they said together.

"Isn't it great, boys?" Donald said. "It's a trailer with every modern appliance! This is the only way to go camping these days!"

"But we wanted to go camping in the old-fashioned way," Huey said. "With just our Junior Woodchuck camping gear!"

"Yeah, Uncle Donald," Dewey added. "We want to earn our merit badges and become members of the J.W.L.O.C."

"What's that?"

"The Junior Woodchuck Loyal Order of

Campers," Huey explained.

"You'll earn your badges," Donald said. "But you'll be a lot more comfortable in this trailer while you do."

Soon, Donald and the boys were heading toward the mountains. They drove for hours.

Finally they stopped at a campsite in the woods.

"We're going to set up our camp," Huey said.

"That's not for me!" Donald said. "I'm sleeping in my trailer under an electric blanket."

Donald was busy inside his trailer. He opened cans of food with his electric can opener. He heated the food on his electric stove. And he watched a rerun of "Ducksmoke" on TV.

Meanwhile, the kids put up a tent and rolled out their sleeping bags. Then they made a campfire.

"Dinner's ready!" Donald yelled from the door of the trailer. "Hot dogs, beans, and root beer!"

"Aw, gee, Uncle Donald! We wanted to fix dinner over our campfire!" Huey said.

"Nonsense!" Donald said. "Why do it the hard way? It's a lot easier using my modern gadgets. Now quit grumbling and come to dinner!"

The four of them were just finishing their root beer when the trailer lights went out.

The first voice out of the darkness was Huey's: "What happened to the lights?"

"There must be something wrong with the wiring," Donald answered.

"We have a lantern outside," Dewey said. He brought the lantern inside and handed it to Donald.

"This is so old-fashioned!" Donald said. "But I'll only need it for a minute. I'll have this problem fixed in a second."

The boys left their uncle studying the fuse box and went back to their campfire. In a little

while, Donald came out
of the trailer.

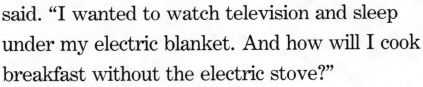

"Doggone stupid
thing!" he shouted.

"What's wrong,
Uncle Donald?" asked
Louie.

"The battery in the
trailer is dead," Donald
said. "I wanted to watch television and sleep
under my electric blanket. And how will I cook
breakfast without the electric stove?"

"Now, calm down, Uncle Donald," Huey
said. "Tomorrow morning you can take the car
back to town and get a new battery for the
trailer!"

"I guess that's what I'll have to do," Donald
said. "But now I'm going to bed. I'm sleeping
in the car. If I can't look at TV, at least I can
listen to the car radio!"

The mountain air was getting cooler. Louie,
Huey, and Dewey crawled into their sleeping
bags. In a moment, they were fast asleep.

Donald switched on the radio. He leaned
back and closed his eyes. He was put to sleep

by the music of the Duckburg Symphony.

Donald woke up the next morning to the
smell of bacon frying. "Wake up, Uncle
Donald. Breakfast is ready," Huey called.
Donald sat up. Outside he could see the kids

cooking breakfast over a campfire.

"No thanks, boys," he said. "I'm going to wait until I get a new camper battery. Then I can cook up a real fancy breakfast for myself! Hurry up and eat so we can go into town."

After the boys finished breakfast, they all piled into the car. Donald put the key in and turned it to "start." Nothing happened. He tried again. Nothing happened. The car battery was dead.

"I don't believe it!" moaned Donald. "Why did this happen to me?"

"Well, you left the car radio on all night and wore out the battery," Huey said.

"This is terrible!" Donald groaned. "We're miles from town. Without a car! Without an electric stove! We're ruined!"

"Take it easy, Uncle Donald," Huey said. "The first rule of the J.W.L.O.C. is 'DON'T PANIC!' "

"We'll just hike to town," Louie added.
Donald didn't have much choice, so he
followed his nephews into the woods.

"The town is to the east," Louie said.

"And which way is that?" Donald asked.

Dewey pointed to the sunrise. "The sun rises in the east," he explained.

By noon, Donald was starved and exhausted. "Hold it, boys!" he gasped. "I've got to rest!"

He made his way through tall bushes, looking for a spot to sit down. Suddenly, he felt himself sliding down a steep cliff. "Yeow!" he yelled. His nephews ran over and looked down. Donald was sitting at the bottom of the hill. He was holding his ankle and screaming loudly.

"I think you've sprained your ankle, Uncle," Dewey said after he had looked at it. "We'll have to carry you!"

"How are you going to do that?" Donald asked. "You'll need a stretcher."

"Just leave that to the J.W.L.O.C.," Huey

said. "Dewey, you and Louie go find two long poles. I'll dip my hanky in that stream over there and wrap it around Uncle Donald's ankle."

The boys found two poles. They bandaged Donald's ankle. Then they made a stretcher out of the poles and their shirts. They lifted Donald onto the stretcher and carried him out of the woods.

A week later, Donald was back on his feet. The boys had been awarded their J.W.L.O.C.

merit badges. The trailer had a new battery.

"I'm sorry I spoiled your camping trip, boys," Donald said.

"You didn't spoil anything, Uncle Donald," Huey said.

"We never would have won our merit badges *without* you!" Louie said.

"That's right," Dewey said. "Going camping with you, Uncle, proved that we could handle *any* problem in the woods!"

"Come Play with Me!"

In most museums, visitors just look at all the things the museum has. But the Children's Museum in Boston, Massachusetts, is different. In this museum, kids can play with everything they see. Here are some of the fun things you can do and see in this museum.

On this phone, you can push buttons with your toes.

A milk bottle three stories high sells ice cream.

The Giant's Desktop is 12 times bigger than a normal desktop. So is everything on it. The paper clips, pencils, coffee cup, and ruler are all giant size. You can walk on top of the desk. You can jump up and down on the buttons on

*Grandparents' House is a model of a
19th-century home.*

the telephone. You can also try to write with a
huge pencil.

 Grandparents' House is a model of an old
house. You can sew on an old sewing machine
in the attic. You can open the trunks and try

on the old clothes. If you want, you can sit in the parlor and read a book or play a big radio. In the kitchen you will see how people used to cook and wash dishes. You can even use the old tools in grandfather's cellar.

The *Japanese House* is a real house. It was built about 150 years ago in Japan. The two-story house has six rooms and a bathroom and kitchen. There is even a small garden with plants and statues. Classes at the museum teach people about life in Japan. You can learn how to make Japanese things, like noodles, straw mats, kites, and paper screens.

In the *Factory*, you can be a worker in a company that makes toy spinning tops. You may choose from a number of different jobs.

The Japanese house and shop are 150 years old.

You can stamp circles out of cardboard or you can put wooden pegs through the holes in each cardboard circle. You can work in the department that ships the toys to stores. Or you can help to make out workers' salary checks. In the *Factory*, you will get an idea of what it's like to go to work every day, the way adults do.

City Slice has a house and car that have been cut open. You can see how they were put together. It also has part of a city street. You can work the traffic light and climb down a manhole.

In the cutaway house, you can see the inside of everything.

The *Computer Center* has 12 computers for children to use. At the center, you can find out exactly how a computer works. And you can play games like tic-tac-toe on a computer. You can also play with a toy turtle that only moves when the computer tells it to move.

Garbage is turned into art in the recycling room.

The museum also has a *TV Studio*. In the studio, you can operate the TV camera. Or you sit behind a microphone and pretend that you are giving the news. As you do this, you will appear on a TV screen in the studio.

There are many other things you can do in the Boston Children's Museum. You can make movies. You can use tools like drills and saws. In the natural history corner, you can study the habits of common city animals. Here you can watch mice, ants, worms, and cockroaches doing all the things they do naturally.

The museum will also show you how to use materials that have been thrown away as garbage. This is called *recycling*. The materials may be pieces of wood, foam, paper, or plastic. Probably they were thrown away by factories or business. The museum will teach you how to use them to make new things. You might make a sculpture of an animal from them. Or you might make a useful object such as a cup or box. Or you might use them in a science project. The lesson of recycling is that many things we throw away should be saved.

A day at the Boston Children's Museum is a wonderful way to have fun and learn at the same time.

A TWO-MILE HOT DOG

Here are some facts about food that may surprise you.

Big Eater

The biggest hot dog ever made was two miles long and weighed over 2,000 pounds. It was cooked and served at a children's party in Hyde Park in London, England, in May 1974.

Babe Ruth once ate 20 hot dogs just before he played in a baseball game.

Milk Machine

A cow usually produces about 62 glasses of milk a day. But in 1975 a cow in Indiana produced 372 glasses in one day—a new record.

Counting Chickens

A hen lays about 240 eggs a year.

Each person in the United States eats an

average of 37 pounds of chicken a year.

There are more chickens in the world than people.

Tomato Tale

Thomas Jefferson was the third president of the United States. Before he became president, he was one of the first people in the United States to grow tomatoes. He didn't eat them though. He used them to decorate other food.

In Jefferson's time, people thought that if they ate a tomato they would die. A man named Colonel Robert G. Johnson didn't believe this. He decided to prove that tomatoes were good to eat.

On September 26, 1820, he stood on the steps of a building in Salem, New Jersey.

Hundreds of people watched as he ate a basketful of tomatoes. They thought he was poisoning himself. But he didn't even get sick.

Watery Foods

Can you name some foods that have a lot of water in them? Watermelon, oranges, and tomatoes are a few. But did you know that bread is more than one-third water? Meat is more than half water. And milk and juice are nearly all water.

Food Firsts

The first bakery opened over 2,000 years ago in Italy. It sold honey-wheat bread.

Lemonade was first made in France in 1603.

The first pizza parlor in the United States opened in New York City in 1905.

Bibbidi-
Bobbidi-
Who?

Cinderella was in the kitchen of the castle. She was making breakfast for her friends, the birds and mice. But where were her two favorite mice? "It's not like Jack and Gus to be late," she said to herself.

Suddenly two tiny mice ran into the kitchen. "Cinderelly, Cinderelly! Upystairs! Upystairs! Stepsisties!" Jack said very fast.

"Oh, please slow down, Jack. You know it's hard for me to understand the way you talk," Cinderella said.

Just then, a small, plump figure hurried into

the room. It was Cinderella's fairy godmother.

"What could have happened to it?" the fairy godmother said. "I had my magic wand with me when I arrived. And now I can't find it!"

Jack and Gus were still talking quickly. Gus tugged at Cinderella's skirts.

"What are you two up to now?" asked Cinderella as Jack and Gus tried to pull her toward the stairs.

"I wonder if they know something about my wand," the fairy godmother said.

Cinderella and her fairy godmother started

for the stairs. From a room upstairs, they could hear the sound of a loud fight. They tiptoed up and looked into the room from the door.

"Give it to me, Drizella," Anastasia shouted. "You haven't been able to make it work. Now give me a chance."

Drizella ran away from her sister and waved the wand in the air. "Hobbidy-bobbidy-zoo, fill my pockets with gold!" she said.

Drizella stuck her hand into her pocket. But all she found were wet goldfish. "Ugh! What's wrong with this thing? I wished for gold jewelry, not goldfish!"

Anastasia grabbed
the wand from her
sister. "You can't do
anything right!" She
waved the wand above
her head. "I wish for a
beautiful fur coat.
Hippity-hoppity-doo!"

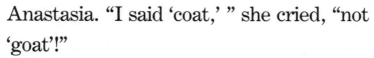

In a flash, a billy goat
appeared before
Anastasia. "I said 'coat,' " she cried, "not
'goat'!"

"Thank goodness they haven't found out the
magic words!" Cinderella's godmother said.
"We must get the wand back before they do.
Once they guess the words, the wand will
grant all their wishes. And I don't think I will
be able to change the spells!"

Just then, Cinderella's stepsisters saw
Cinderella and the fairy godmother standing in
the doorway. "What are you doing here?"
Anastasia shouted.

"Anastasia, Drizella," Cinderella said. "You
know that wand doesn't belong to you! Please

return it before you hurt someone!"

Drizella laughed. "Listen to Miss Goody-goody. You've got everything you want—the prince, the castle, everything!" She slammed the door in their faces.

Cinderella pushed open her stepsisters' door. But the room was empty. "Oh, no," she sighed. "They're not here! They must have gone out the other door. We'll have to search the castle. I'll take the top floors. Godmother, you look on this floor. Jack and Gus, you take the first floor."

The stepsisters were down in the castle's

kitchen. Here, many cooks stirred and tasted while the fat master chef watched. Lucifer the cat waited to catch any food that fell to the floor.

"Mmm! Everything smells so good," Anastasia said. "I think I'll have something to eat!"

"You're always hungry," Drizella said. "Well, go on, eat! While you're making a pig of yourself, I'll make this stupid wand work. Oh, what are those magic words?"

Drizella began calling out all the words she could think of: "Clippity-cloppity-boo! Snippety-snappity-loo! Pippity-poppity-poo!" Nothing happened.

Drizella threw the wand to the ground. "I've had enough of this," she said. "Good-bye, and a bibbidi-bobbidi-boo to you! I think I'll have something to eat, too."

Just by chance, Drizella had spoken the magic words! The wand jumped to life. It rose slowly into the air. The room was filled with a rainbow of magic dust. Then, strange things began to happen.

Lids rose off the pots on the stove and sailed through the air. Cakes in the ovens suddenly blew up. "What's going on here?" the fat chef demanded. "I won't have this kind of trouble in my kitchen!"

The wand lifted the plump chef up and put him right into a sink full of dish water!

"The magic words! You finally found them!" Anastasia cried. "Tell me what they are!"

"That's my secret, sister dear," Drizella said.

"But first we have to get that wand back." The stepsisters began to chase the wand as it sailed around the kitchen.

Just then, Jack and Gus arrived in the kitchen.

"Oh, no!" Jack squeaked. "Look like stepsisties found magic words. Quick! We get Cinderelly!" They ran off.

A moment later, Drizella reached high in the

air and grabbed the wand. "There! Now I have my wand back," she said.

Cinderella and the fairy godmother appeared, led by Jack and Gus. "Oh, it's you again," Drizella said. "Well, now I know the magic words. I'll put an end to your trouble-making once and for all." She pointed the wand at Cinderella and the fairy godmother. Then she began to chant: "These two are trouble for me and for you . . ."

"Gus, we got to do something before she makes that spell," Jack said.

"I know!" said Gus. "Here, Lucifee! Here, kitty, kitty!"

The cat turned his attention from the food

and ran after Gus. Lucifer had never been able to catch Gus.

Drizella still said her spell: ". . . change them to toads, that's what I'll do . . ."

The two mice ran across the kitchen with the cat racing after them.

Gus ran under Drizella's skirts. She was just finishing the spell: ". . . bibbidi-bobbidi-boo!"

Trying to catch Gus, Lucifer crashed right into Drizella. This made her fall backward. She let go of the wand. It flew up in the air and landed in the hands of the fairy godmother. And now it was pointing right at Cinderella's stepsisters!

In a second, they were turned into two ugly
green toads.

"This is all your fault," said the toad
Anastasia to Drizella. "I never should have
listened to you."

Now Lucifer saw the two toads. He forgot
all about Jack and Gus. He began to chase the

two toads out of the kitchen.

"Godmother!" cried Cinderella. "You must change them back before Lucifer catches them!"

"Don't worry," the fairy godmother said with a smile. "Lucifer has gotten so fat on castle cream he can't catch anything. I'll change them back. But not until those two have learned their lesson. This should teach them never to steal a magic wand."

Animals in Danger

Pandas and sea turtles are very different from each other. Pandas have fur on their bodies. Pandas live on the land. Sea turtles have a thick shell on their bodies. Sea turtles live in the ocean.

Pandas and sea turtles have the same problem. They are two of the animals in the world that are in danger of dying out. Many kinds of animals that once lived on earth no longer are alive. The dinosaur is one example. When all the animals of a certain kind have died and no new ones are born, then that animal is *extinct*. This means that this animal will never live again.

Why do animals become extinct? Sometimes people cause them to die out. People have destroyed the forests where pandas live. People have killed sea turtles for their meat and to get their shells.

Left: People have destroyed the forests where pandas live.
Below: People have killed sea turtles for their meat.

Other people—scientists—are trying to save these animals. The world would be a sadder place if either the panda or the sea turtle became extinct. Here is what we would lose:

The Giant Panda

This black and white creature is one of the world's most loved animals. The panda looks like a bear, but it is actually more like a raccoon. A giant panda weighs up to 300 pounds when it is grown. Pandas live in thick mountain forests in China.

Also in Danger

The California condor is the biggest bird in North America. Its wings may measure nine feet from tip to tip. It eats only the flesh of dead animals. There are only about 30 California condors alive today.

Pandas are shy animals. They live alone. They are also night creatures. During the day, they sleep in trees. A panda curls up so that it can use its tail as a pillow, or to cover its face.

A panda is very tiny when it is born. But it spends much of its time eating, and it grows quickly. The mother plays with her baby. She tosses it from arm to arm. She tickles it. Sometimes she even plays peekaboo with it.

The giant panda is the favorite animal of the Chinese people. In China, some pandas have

Also in Danger

Manatees are large gray mammals. They eat plants in the sea. Manatees have been hunted for their meat and skins. Now they are protected by law. But no one knows how many manatees are left in the world.

given birth to babies in zoos. In a zoo, the babies can grow to be adults and perhaps have children of their own.

No one knows how many pandas there are in the world. But scientists believe there are not even 1,000.

Sea Turtles

There are seven types of sea turtles. Six of these types are in danger of becoming extinct. Sea turtles are large creatures. Some weigh 500 pounds or more.

Baby sea turtles are born inside of eggs. The mother digs a hole in the sand on the beach. Then she lays her eggs. She covers the eggs with sand. Then she leaves. When the babies are ready to come out, their shells crack open and they crawl out. They head for the water. But since their mothers are not there to protect them, many of the babies die.

Scientists are now trying to raise baby sea turtles in captivity. They protect the babies until they are old enough to protect themselves. Then they are put back in the ocean. In this way, scientists hope to increase the number of sea turtles in the world.

CORAL RAINBOWS UNDER THE SEA

Coral makes the ocean beautiful. It grows on the bottom of the sea. Undersea plants, animals, and fish live in coral homes.

Coral is made from the skeleton of a tiny sea animal called a coral *polyp*. Most animals have either bones or shells, which are called

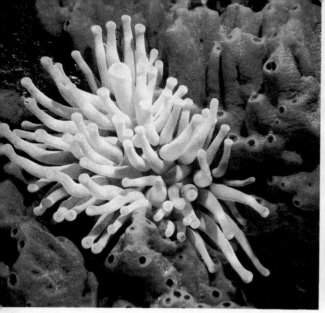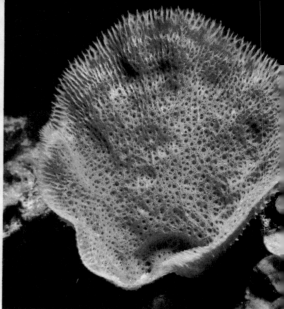

The rainbow of color in a coral reef includes white sea anemones (left) and purple sponges (right).

skeletons. A skeleton gives an animal its shape and also protects it. Human beings have skeletons inside their bodies. Coral polyps, in contrast, have skeletons outside their bodies.

A coral polyp looks like a cup. A coral polyp has a mouth that is surrounded by tiny arms called *tentacles*. The tentacles reach out of the cup and catch food for the coral polyp. The food it catches is tiny ocean life. The moving water on the bottom of the ocean carries this food from one place to another.

There are many different kinds of coral polyps. Each kind is a different size, a different shape, and a different color. Coral can be found in every color of the rainbow—red, green, orange, blue, yellow, and many others.

Coral grows in many different shapes. Some corals look like tree branches, flowers, or mushrooms. Many corals are named for the unusual shapes they form. One kind of coral is named brain coral. It looks like the brain of an animal. Another kind is named star coral. Its shape suggests a star shining in the sky at night. Still another coral is called staghorn coral. It looks like the horn of a male deer, called a stag.

Sea creatures like tube worms (left) live in coral formations such as stag coral (right).

Underwater shapes are like those on land. Brain coral (left) looks like an animal brain. Star coral (right) is full of tiny flowers that look like stars.

Most coral polyps live together in bunches on the bottom of the ocean. The polyps attach themselves to one another to make a pile. When a polyp dies, its skeleton remains part of the pile. The pile grows upward and outward as more and more coral skeletons pile up. The pile grows very slowly, only a few inches a year. A large group of coral skeletons is called a *coral reef.* After hundreds of years a coral reef may have grown to a huge size.

A coral reef creates a beautiful underwater *community*, which is like a town. Ocean waves carry tiny plants toward the reef. The plants attach themselves to the reef. They provide food for fish and other sea creatures. These

undersea animals live inside open spaces in the
reef. The reef is a community where plants and
animals need each other. It looks like a
beautiful underwater garden.

Some reefs may be many miles long.
Palancar Reef, off the coast of Mexico, is six
miles long. The coral forms of Palancar Reef
reach up from the floor of the ocean. Strange

Golden coral (above right) does not form reefs. It uses its tentacles (above left) to capture food.

and beautiful creatures swim through this silent underwater world. Sea anemones and many other animals live closely together here, even on top of each other. A sea anemone is another type of polyp. It has tentacles to gather food, like a coral polyp. The sponge is another marine animal that may live in a reef. It is like the sponge you use to wash the dishes.

There are other forms of life on a coral reef. Coral crabs and feather stars are among them. Feather stars look like plants but are actually animals. Coral crabs live in every ocean of the world. They catch food with their claws, called *pincers*.

Many different types of fish also live in and

A coral reef is full of animal life, such as schools of chromis fish (right) and feather stars (left). The feather star looks like a plant but is a sea animal.

*A speckled coral crab rests in
its hiding place in the reef.*

around a coral reef. These fish swim together
in a group called a *school*. They sleep during
the day and come out at night to hunt for food.

The reef community goes through a change
when the sun goes down. Some creatures find
a safe place in the coral and settle down for the
night. But the fish swim out into the open to
begin to look for food. The feather stars put
out their long arms to capture tiny animals that
drift past. Coral polyps all over the reef extend
their tentacles to gather food.

The polyps will not live for a long time. But
the reef will. Long after a polyp has died, its
skeleton remains as part of the coral reef.

Give a Box Some Beans

Now you can keep your favorite things in a beautiful box you make yourself. Here's how to do it.

What You'll Need

    One box with lid (any size)

    Glue

    Poster paint

    Dry foods (macaroni, beans, sunflower seeds, rice, bay leaves, etc.)

    Clear nail polish or acrylic spray

First step: Paint the box with any color poster paint.

Second step: Let the paint dry. Then make a design with beans, seeds, or macaroni on the top of the box.

Third step: Glue the dry foods to the top of
the box.

Fourth step: The dry foods could attract
insects. You may want to protect the design
by sealing it. You can use clear nail polish or
an acrylic spray or sealer. Cover the top of
the box with the nail polish or acrylic spray.

The Spookiest Park

Imagine that you are walking through a clearing in the woods. There are many large rocks in the clearing. Walking along, you get a spooky feeling. Suddenly you realize that these are not just rocks. They are huge monsters!

But thank goodness they're not alive! You are actually in a place called the Park of Monsters to the north of Rome, the capital city of Italy. The monsters in this park are all harmless carvings. An artist carved them out of rocks hundreds of years ago. The art of carving figures from stone is called *sculpting*. The type of artist who does this is a *sculptor*, and his artwork is *sculpture*.

An Italian prince named Vicino Orsini designed the park over 300 years ago. The sculptor carved most of them out of the boulders that were already in the park. Many of the sculptures are so large that people can walk inside of them. Many look like giants and

Left: What's inside the mouth? Walk in to find out.
Below: The statues were carved out of giant rocks.

dangerous animals. But others look like
ordinary things. One sculpture looks like a
huge woman with a bowl on her head. Others
seem to be creatures from fairy tales.

And none of the "monsters" can move or
speak. Children visiting the park can touch,
climb on, and even walk inside the monsters.
The monsters never complain.

PAINT
A GLASS

It's fun and easy to turn old jars and bottles
into bright-colored treasures.

What You'll Need

Bottles and jars that held food and
    liquids
Waterproof paint in several colors—red,
    yellow, green, blue, black, white
Paint brush
Paper and pencil

First step: On a piece of paper, draw the shape of the bottle or plate you're going to paint. Then draw a design inside the lines of that shape.

A design can be made of flowers or fish or smiling faces, just like the ones you see on the bottles on these pages. Or you can copy designs you like from books or magazines. The plate you see on the next page is decorated with designs that have special meaning for farmers in Pennsylvania. The sun and raindrops are for healthy crops.

Second step: Tape the paper on the inside of the bowl or jar you want to paint. You will be able to see the design through the glass. Now paint the design on the outside. Use the design taped on the inside as a guide for your paint brush.

Here are some other tips:

1. Wash the glasssware very well. The glass must be clean, or the paint won't stick to it.

2. Dry the glassware very well. If it's wet,

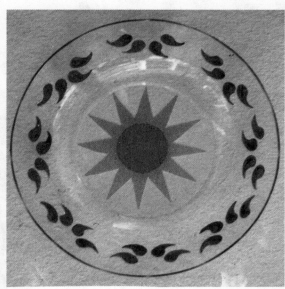

the paint will run.

3. Don't touch where you have painted. This will leave fingerprints.

4. Keep a piece of wet paper towel handy when you paint. If you make a mistake, you can wipe the paint off quickly.

5. Let the paint dry completely. Then, if the colors aren't as dark as you like, put on more paint.

Pinocchio Goes to Sea

Geppetto looked at Pinocchio's report card. Pinocchio's grades were very bad.

"Pinocchio, you must study more," Geppetto said. "You'll never grow up to be a shopkeeper or wood carver if you can't read and add and subtract."

"I don't want to be a shopkeeper," the little puppet said. "I want to be a sailor."

"Oh ho," Geppetto said. "So that's what this is all about. You don't like school anymore. You only like the book *Treasure Island* and pirates and sailors. Well, I'm not going to read *Treasure Island* to you anymore until your grades are better."

Pinocchio went to his room to do his homework. But all he thought about was how he would like to sail the high seas.

Pinocchio woke up early in the morning.

"Hey, Jiminy!" he cried. The cricket sat up
in his matchbox bed and rubbed his eyes.

"What is it, Pinocchio?"

"I've just had a great dream. We were
sailors, and we found Treasure Island. There
were wonderful jewels hanging from every
tree and there were piles of gold everywhere."

"It was only a dream," Jiminy said, yawning.
"Go back to sleep."

Pinocchio jumped out of his bed. He began
opening drawers and putting clothes into his
pillowcase. "Come on, Jiminy," he said, "we're
going to sea!"

It was daylight when they reached the

harbor. A ship with three sails was tied up at the end of the dock. To Pinocchio it looked just like the ship in *Treasure Island*. He could see the crew climbing the masts. The ship was getting ready to sail.

Pinocchio ran down the dock. A tall man in a black coat was standing at the gangplank shouting orders.

"I want to join your crew," Pinocchio said.

The captain looked down at the small boy. "Can you read a map or a compass? Can you tell where a ship is by looking at the stars?" he asked.

Pinocchio was about to answer, "Yes." Then he remembered what happened to his nose when he lied.

"No," the puppet said honestly.

"Can you write well enough to keep the ship's records?" asked the captain.

"Not that well,"

Pinocchio said.

The captain frowned. "If you can't read and write and add and subtract, there's only one job for you. So follow me."

The captain led Pinocchio up the gangplank.

He ordered the ship to set sail. Sailors hurried to pull up the anchor and throw off the lines. No one noticed the small, green cricket hop aboard and hide behind some rope piles.

Pinocchio followed the captain below the deck to the ship's kitchen. "This is your new helper," the captain told the ship's cook.

The cook was a short, red-faced man. He raced around the kitchen shouting orders at Pinocchio.

"Put that pan there! Put that pot here! Not there, wooden head, here!"

When the pots and pans were put away, the cook led Pinocchio to a huge bag of potatoes.

He handed the puppet a knife. "Peel," he ordered.

"All of them?" Pinocchio asked.

"All of them," snapped the cook. "And then there are pots to wash and the deck to scrub."

After three days of this kind of work, Pinocchio was a mess. His arms and his back

hurt. "This isn't my idea of sailing," he said.

Pinocchio was nearly finished peeling potatoes when he heard the sailors shouting. He dropped his knife and ran up to the deck.

One of the men had caught a large sea turtle in a net. He lifted it aboard and the crew cheered.

"Turtle soup for dinner, lads," yelled the cook. "I'll be back with me knives."

The sailors turned the turtle onto its back. The turtle waved its legs wildly.

Pinocchio watched the turtle trying to turn over. "You're a prisoner on this ship, too," he thought.

The crew was happy thinking about turtle soup for dinner. The captain's shout of "Avast!" surprised them. "Take down the sails," the captain shouted. The crew rushed to obey.

A storm was coming up. The turtle was

forgotten as the crew went to work.

But Pinocchio hadn't forgotten the turtle. The crew was so busy they never noticed Pinocchio push the turtle across the deck. The turtle's shell scraped on the wood floor. But Pinocchio slowly moved the turtle over to the gangway opening. With one last push he was able to get the turtle over the side. It landed in the water with a great splash.

"Quick! In here," called a friendly voice. Pinocchio looked around.

Jiminy Cricket was sitting on the edge of an empty barrel. Pinocchio climbed inside, and the two friends clung to each other at the bottom of the barrel.

The sky grew black, and the ship shook all over. Lightning lit up the sky. Rain poured into the barrel. Suddenly a huge wave crashed down on the ship. It swept the barrel over the side and into the water. Luck was with Pinocchio and Jiminy. The barrel landed right-side-up.

The two friends spent a wet night in the barrel, splashed by the waves. At last morning came, and the sea became calm.

Pinocchio looked over the top of the barrel. He saw a bright green head peeking out from under a broad green shell. There were scrape marks on the turtle's shell. It was the same turtle that Pinocchio had saved.

"He's come to save us," Jiminy said.

They climbed out of the barrel and onto the turtle's back. The turtle began swimming. Before long, Pinocchio and Jiminy were safe on shore. They waved happily at the turtle as it swam back to sea.

Pinocchio and Jiminy made their way back to Geppetto's shop. They were wet but safe.

Geppetto greeted them with tears and hugs.

Pinocchio told him about their troubles.
Geppetto said, "Well, I hope that now you'll
stop dreaming about the sea and do your
homework."

And that's exactly what happened.
Pinocchio's grades got better. He even won a
prize for turning in the most book reports.

Still, Geppetto was not surprised that
Pinocchio never wrote a book report on
Treasure Island.

Making Friends with a Shark

Sometimes a large fish or animal and a small fish or animal become partners. They help each other.

The ocean can be dangerous for little fish. Big fish like to eat little fish. One very smart little fish has made the shark his friend. The little fish is the pilotfish. It swims beside the big shark. Big fish will not hurt the pilotfish.

They are afraid to get too close to the shark.

The shark does not try to eat the pilotfish because the pilotfish helps the shark. It eats the tiny animals that stick to the shark's body. These tiny animals are called *parasites*. They can hurt the shark if they are not removed.

Some crabs and sponges become partners. First the sponge crab finds a sponge. Then the crab puts the sponge on its head. Tiny hairs on

Left: Tiny pilotfish swim alongside a giant shark.
Below: A grenadier crab holds anemones in its claws.

the crab's shell make the sponge stick. The sponge grows bigger and covers the crab. Sea animals like to eat crabs, but they don't like to eat sponges. So the crab is safe.

The crab helps the sponge by giving it a ride along the ocean floor. As they move, water goes through the sponge. The water has food in it that the sponge can eat.

Grenadier crabs become partners with tiny sea animals called sea anemones. The crabs carry the sea anemones in their claws. The crabs push the anemones into the faces of their enemies to keep them away. The anemones carry poison, and other sea animals are afraid of them.

Birds and animals also help each other. Egrets are birds with long necks and long legs. They hop onto the backs of water buffalo and rhinoceroses. The animals walk through the grass and this makes the bugs fly up. The egrets quickly eat the bugs. The egrets warn the animals they ride on of danger. They fly away when they see an enemy.

Zebras and ostriches are another friendly

A sponge crab carries a sponge on its back.

pair. Ostriches have good eyes. They see
enemies before zebras can. But a zebra can
smell some enemies before the ostrich can see
them. So the two animals warn each other of
danger.

People and animals can also help each other.
Watch dogs and seeing-eye dogs are two
examples. Can you think of other partnerships
between people and animals?

The
Enchanted
Figs

A long time ago, in a faraway kingdom, a
queen lived alone with her son and daughter,
Prince Victor and Princess Victoria.

The queen was not rich. She didn't have
enough gold to keep a large army. So she

thought of a very special way to guard her kingdom. She hired a wandering wizard or magician. The wizard planted a ring of magical fig trees around the kingdom. Whoever looked at one of these enchanted trees would fall under a spell and eat one of the figs. And whoever ate one of the figs would quickly turn into a sheep.

The wizard gave the queen one more gift. It was a magic jewel, a moonstone on a gold chain. "When you walk up to the fig trees," the wizard told the queen, "hold this magic jewel up in front of you. Then repeat these rhymes."

The first rhyme stopped the magic spell from working. The second rhyme reversed the spell. It changed a sheep back into a person.

Only four people knew the secret of the rhymes: the queen, her son, her daughter, and Don Pedro, the royal advisor.

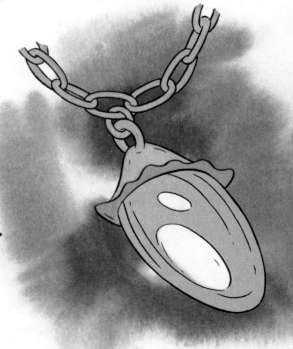

Now the queen thought that she was safe
from King Carlos, her worst enemy. King
Carlos ruled a kingdom close to the queen's.
She sent a message to him. She told him that
great harm would come to his army if he tried
to invade her kingdom. But King Carlos didn't
believe her. He ordered his army to attack.
The army came to the ring of enchanted fig
trees. Every soldier fell under the spell and ate
a fig. The entire army was turned into a flock
of sheep.

Queen Maria now owned many sheep. Soon
she had a good wool business and a lot of gold.
This made the royal advisor, Don Pedro, very

jealous. "Why should she have all that gold?"
he asked himself. And then he thought of a plot
to take over the kingdom.

"I'll get rid of those two brats first," he told
himself. "Then I'll get the queen out of the
way, and I'll be king."

Don Pedro waited in the palace until
everyone was asleep. Then he sneaked into the
queen's bedroom and stole her magic
moonstone. He went to the prince's bedroom.
He knocked out the sleeping prince with a boot
heel. Then he carried him down to the
courtyard. He did the same to the princess.

Don Pedro loaded the prince and princess
onto a horse and led it to the enchanted fig
trees. He held up the
queen's moonstone and
said the spell:

Magic fig,
     your spell deny—
let me pass
     you safely by.

Now he was safe from the spell. But the prince and princess were not. He threw them to the ground and left them alone.

With good luck, Prince Victor woke up in time to hear Don Pedro recite the rhyme. He knew what the advisor was trying to do. He carefully kept his eyes tightly shut. But the princess was not so lucky. When she opened her eyes, she fell under the spell, ate a fig, and turned into a little gray lamb. When the prince touched his sister, he found she was all woolly fluff.

"How awful," said the prince, his eyes still closed. "The only hope we have is to get help from King Alfonso, our mother's friend."

The next morning the prince and the little gray lamb arrived at King Alfonso's castle. Prince Victor told him what had happened. "I never did trust that advisor," Alfonso said. "You may be sure he has told your mother some tall tale about how you've run away. He's probably plotting to get your mother out of the

way, too. Then he'll be king."

"I have a plan, Sire," the prince said. "Would you send for your secretary?"

"Of course, my boy," the king answered.

The prince dictated a letter to the secretary. The letter ended: "The boy seems highly confused, Your Majesty. And he has a pet lamb with him that he keeps calling 'Victoria.' Please, Madame, you must advise me what to do."

"Now King Alfonso," the prince said, "kindly sign this and we'll send it to my mother."

"But your mother will never receive it," the king said. "Don Pedro will get it first."

"That's what I'm hoping," Prince Victor said. "Then he'll hurry here to finish us off. But we'll be ready for him. Now let me tell you your part in my plan."

The next day, Don Pedro arrived at King

Alfonso's castle.

"Oh, Don Pedro," cried King Alfonso, "I hope you've come to tell me what to do about poor Prince Victor."

"Yes, Sire," Don Pedro said. "Queen Maria sent me. She received your letter. I'm here to bring her son back."

"I'll have the boy brought here," Alfonso said. "Meanwhile, why don't you have some of this wine?"

Holding the wine glass, King Alfonso walked toward Don Pedro. But suddenly King Alfonso tripped. His hand reached out for support and grabbed the heavy gold chain holding the moonstone the advisor was wearing. The chain

wasn't strong enough to break his fall. The king crashed to the floor with the chain and moonstone in his hand.

"How clumsy of me," he said. "I'll have this fixed right away." He handed the jewel to a servant before Don Pedro could say no.

In a few minutes the servant returned with the chain and moonstone. "All fixed," King Alfonso said, smiling.

Just then, the prince and the little lamb
were brought into the chamber. Don Pedro
looked relieved. He was anxious to be gone.

"We'll be leaving now," he said, grabbing the
prince. "We mustn't keep the queen waiting."

Outside, Don Pedro lifted the prince into his
cart, whipped the horses, and rushed off. The
little lamb trailed behind, trying to keep up.

Soon they reached the grove of enchanted fig
trees. Don Pedro raised the magic moonstone
and recited the rhyme. But even while he was

reciting it, he felt a strong desire to eat a fig.

He quickly realized what had happened.
"I've been tricked," he shouted. "This isn't the
magic moonstone!" But it was too late.

Prince Victor watched happily as the advisor
ran up to a tree and quickly ate a fig.

In a second, Don Pedro was turned into a
sheep.

Just then the little gray lamb trotted up.
"Oh, there you are, Victoria," the prince called.
He recited the rhyme that would free Victoria
from the fig tree's spell:

Fig of power, I've found the knack—
reverse your spell and turn her back.

Then the prince and the princess climbed up
into the cart and set off for home. Soon they
were together again with their mother, and
they lived happily ever after.